Preface

The main aim of this booklet is to entertain and amuse readers of all ages, especially adolescents and those who are young at heart.

The nursery rhymes of childhood were fun, especially when you sang the words and did the actions. Happy memories indeed. In this selection, written for more mature singers, you will find familiar titles alongside a few new ones, all listed in alphabetical order. In the world of make-believe, imagination knows no bounds.

May your chuckles be many and your disappointments few.

Peter Freeland

Baa, Baa, Blacksheep

Baa, baa, black sheep, are you lamb or mutton?
It doesn't matter very much if you're a greedy glutton.
Roast for the master, hot-pot for the dame.
But hard cheese greedy little boy
Who lives just down the lane.

Bobby Shaftoe's Gone to Sea

Bobby Shaftoe's gone to sea
To catch fishes for my tea.
He'll come back with two or three.
Good old Bobby Shaftoe.

Bobby Shaftoe caught a sprat.
Put it in a linen sack.
Just the right size for the cat.
Thoughtful Bobby Shaftoe.

Bobby Shaftoe saw a shark,
In the evening, almost dark.
Tried to land it for a lark.
Stupid Bobby Shaftoe.

Bobby Shaftoe was well tanned.
By salt breezes he'd been fanned.
Now his boat lies there unmanned.
Poor old Bobby Shaftoe.

Cross Patch

Cross patch, lift the latch
And let the neighbours in.
Gossip and moan until they go home
And add your bit of spin.

Daisy, Daisy

Daisy, Daisy, give me a gentle 'moo'.
I went crazy buying a cow like you.
If long licking tongues should mutter
"He loves her cream and butter".
Just give me milk, as smooth as silk,
In a cattle shed built for two.

Diddle, Diddle, Dumpling, My Son John

Diddle, diddle, dumpling, my son John,
Ate so much he put weight on.
Deaf to all who did advise
No more puddings, cakes or pies.

Doctor, Doctor

Doctor, doctor, when you're ill,
Do you grab the nearest pill?
"From my medical confection,
I just jab the first injection."

Doctor Fell

I do not need thee Doctor Fell,
When I'm feeling fit and well.
But as I'm feeling very sick,
I hope you'll see me pretty quick.

Eeny, Meeny, Miny, Moe

Eeny, meeny, miny, moe.
A wasp has settled on my toe.
If it stings, I'll let you know.
Eeny, meeny, miny, moe.

Elsie Marley

Elsie Marley grew so fine,
And still looks good at ninety-nine.
Much fortified by gin and wine,
Her paint and powder roll back time.

Frog Went A-Wooing

A frog he would a-wooing go,
Whether his mother would let him or no.
So off he set in his very best hat.
What will his girlfriend think about that?

"Won't you take off your hat and stay for a while?"
His girlfriend said with a bit of a smile.
At that the frog began to take fright.
He took up his hat and wished her goodnight.

But as he hopped slowly over a brook,
A very large goose emerged from a nook.
"It's no good trying to run home to mummy,
For later tonight you'll lie deep in my tummy."

With a Roley, Poley, Gammon and Spinach.
"Heigh-ho" says Anthony Rowley.

Hark, Hark, The Dogs Do Bark

Hark, hark, the dogs do bark,
A dog show is coming to town.
To win the first prize you need googly eyes,
And a sweet smiling face, not a frown.
Then hold your tail high and reach for the sky
When the judge looks you up and then down.

Here We Go Round the Mulberry Bush

Here we go round the mulberry bush.
If grandma slows down, we'll give her a push.
If grandad is struggling, gasping for air,
We'll let him withdraw and sit over there.
But what shall we do with our supercharged kiddie?
We'll go round and round until he feels giddy.

Hey, Diddle, Diddle

Hey, diddle, diddle,
The cat had a fiddle,
He played it each morning at eight.
This talented pussy
Played Bach and Debussy,
And hoped it might tune up his mate.

Hey, diddle, diddle,
A verse in the middle.
The little dog laughed too soon.
He fancied some fish,
But his dinner dish
Had quietly eloped with the spoon.

Hey, diddle, diddle,
A farcical riddle.
The cow has jumped over the moon.
Quick! Look at the sky,
There's a cow flying by.
I think it's about to land soon.

Hickory, Dickory, Dock

Hickory, dickory, dock
Einstein once said of a clock,
"For good or for ill
At the top of a hill,
It will do a faster tick-tock."

Higgledy, Piggledy

Higgledy, piggledy, my son Fred,
Thought he'd try to shave his head.
But more tricky than he feared,
Got no further than his beard.

Humpty Dumpty

Humpty Dumpty sat on a wall
That was because he was not very tall.
Although he had stood on the ground now and then,
He couldn't see all the king's horses or men.

I Love Little Pussy

I love little pussy,
Her coat is so warm.
She stays close beside me
From evening 'till dawn.

Dear little pussy
Is very well fed,
And when I retire
I take her to bed.

She sleeps on my pillow,
That dear little cat.
Much better, I think,
Than down on the mat.

When pussy wakes up,
Her eyes open wide,
I open the back door
And put her outside.

If All the Seas Were Bread and Cheese

If all the seas were bread and cheese,
And there was nought to drink,
You couldn't sail or row a boat,
But neither could you sink.

Itsy, Bitsy Spider

An itsy, bitsy spider built a funnel web.
In flew a fly and got stuck by its head.
Out popped the spider, as most spiders do,
Put its foot on a sticky thread,
And now it's stuck there too.

Jack and Jill

Jack and Jill went to the mill
To grind a sack of grain.
A mouse that ran between the stones
Was never seen again.

Jack Sprat

Jack Sprat was very fat.
His wife was very lean.
And all their loving little Sprats
Were somewhere in between.

Ladybird, Ladybird

Ladybird, ladybird, fetch me a pill.
I heard on the grapevine your children are ill.
If you don't hurry, they might go to heaven.
One has got five spots, another eleven.

Little Arabella Miller

Little Arabella Miller
Found a furry caterpillar.
Put it on her brother's plate.
What an unexpected fate.

Little Boy Blue

Little boy blue, come blow on your horn.
The valves on your trumpet might be a bit worn:
But needless to say, we'll all stand and gloat,
If sooner or later, you hit the right note.

Little Miss Muffet

Little Miss Muffett went to a buffet
Held in a large marquee tent.
Along came a tiger,
Which sat down beside her.
But nobody saw where she went.

Little Polly Flinders

Little Polly Flinders
Played among the cinders:
But she forgot the coals were hot,
That's why she burnt her fingers.

Lucy Lockett

Lucy Lockett lost her rabbit
Kitty Fisher found it.
It was in the rockery
With several rabbits round it.

Mary Had a Cheshire Cat

Mary had a Cheshire cat,
Its coat as soft as silk.
She fed it on the finest meats
And gave it lots of milk.
It followed her to school one day,
But someone let it in,
And several children ran away,
Scared by its hideous grin.

Mary, Mary Quite Contrary

Mary, Mary quite contrary,
How does your garden grow?
With wasps and bugs and lots of slugs,
And little snails all in a row.

My Dog 'Bing'

I have a dog whose name is 'Bing',
A dog that will eat anything.
And when he isn't chewing toys,
He's very fond of girls and boys.

Oh Dear, What Can the Matter Be?

Oh dear, what can the matter be?
Puffington City were beaten on Saturday:
Too much egotism and flattery
And some decisions weren't fair.

Old King Cole

Old King Cole was a cunning old soul
And a cunning old soul was he.
He called for his phone,
And when he was alone
He called up his fiddlers three.

The first fiddler did fiddle his books
And a very fine fiddler was he.
The second his cash,
While the third made a dash,
Hiding bank notes in an old tree.

In the depths of night, stars shining bright,
The king approached that tree.
He wore his crown
And golden gown,
And called up his fiddlers three.

And as they danced around that tree
They all sang merrily:
"I'm old King Cole,
I'm a cunning old soul
And no one will catch me."

Oh Where Has My Little Dog Gone?

Oh where, oh where, has my little dog gone?
Oh where, oh where, can he be?
He was sniffing around with his nose to the ground,
And heading for a distant tree.

Oh what, oh what, has my little dog seen?
Oh what, oh what, could it be?
He was rather fond of an old muddy pond,
And splashing wet mud over me.

Oh why, oh why, has my little dog barked?
Oh why, oh why, should that be?
The answer to that is a black feral cat,
Perched high on the branch of a tree.

Oh when, oh when, did my little dog roam?
Oh when, oh when, could that be?
He met a retriever and then wouldn't leave her,
But paid no attention to me.

Oh why, oh why, have I left him at home?
Oh why, oh why should that be?
I said "If you roam I will leave you at home,
And you'll go no more 'walkies' with me."

Old Mother Hubbard

Old Mother Hubbard went to the cupboard
To fetch her good doggie a bone:
But when she got there the cupboard was bare.
He'd been to the cupboard alone.

One Potato

One potato, two potatoes, three potatoes, four.
You are bound to put on weight by eating any more.

One, Two, Three, Four, Five

One, two, three, four, five,
Put my hand in a beehive.
Six, seven, eight, nine, ten,
Quickly took it out again.

Pat-a-cake, Pat-a-cake

Pat-a-cake, pat-a-cake, baker's man.
Bake me a burger as fast as you can.
Fill it with chuck mince, chopped onions and thyme.
There's always spare room in that stomach of mine.

Pease Pudding

Pease pudding hot,
Pease pudding cold.
Pease pudding in the pot
Nine days old.
Some like it hot.
Some like it cold.
But nobody wants it
If it's green with mould.

Pop Went the Weasel

Half a pound of very dry rice,
Water and some treacle.
When they mixed in his inside,
Pop went the weasel.

Pussy Cat, Pussy Cat

Pussy cat, pussy cat, where have you been?
In next door's garden, courting a queen.
Pussy cat, pussy cat, what did you there?
I sang pussy love songs in the night air.

Pussy cat, pussy cat, lit by the moon,
Were you rewarded for singing your tune?
Pussies galore, with little to do,
Raced to the garden and said, "we love you."

Ride a Cock Horse

Ride a cock horse
Down a challenging course,
Always treating your horse like a friend.
With the winning post passed,
Never mind you were last.
Only think of the cheers at the end.

Ring-a-Ring O' Roses

Ring-a-ring o' roses,
With scents that charm our noses.
But nature warns
Their prickly thorns
Hurt more than one supposes.

Rock-a-bye Baby

Rock-a-bye baby on the treetop,
Ever so high; a long way to drop.
Poor little child in rain, snow and gale.
Your mummy and daddy will soon be in jail.

Round and Round the Garden

Round and round the garden,
Like a drunken bear.
Not a flower left standing.
Tin cans everywhere.

Rub-a-dub, Dub

Rub-a-dub, dub, a girl with a tub
Is carefully dyeing her hair.
Last week it looked as black as her cat,
But next week it's going to be fair.

The Grand Old Duke of York

The grand old Duke of York,
He had ten thousand men.
He marched them through the river Ouse.
But now he's down to ten.

The Maypole

Dance around the maypole on the first of May:
Do it on the twenty-first and they'll put you away.

There was a Crooked Man

There was a crooked man
Who had a crooked spine.
A crooked surgeon straightened it,
And both are doing fine.

This Little Piggy

This little piggy went to market.
This little piggy stayed at home.
This little piggy had roast pork.
This little piggy had a ham salad with lettuce and tomato,
And this little piggy enjoyed a delicious bacon sandwich on its way home.

The Wise Old Owl

The wise old owl sat on an oak,
The day his tree went up in smoke.
"Oh dear," he thought, "I soon must dash,
Before my oak's reduced to ash."

Three Blind Mice

Three blind mice. See how they run.
They ran to the larder for sugar and spice,
But swallowed a bait that was not very nice:
A mixture of something with oatmeal and rice.
Those poor blind mice.

Twinkle, Twinkle, Little Star

Twinkle, twinkle, little star
In a galaxy afar.
Will you one day score a goal,
Swallowed by a big black hole?

Wee Willy Winkie

Wee Willy Winkie ran through the town
In his silk pyjamas and red dressing gown,
Peering through the windows, rattling all the locks.
And then he made a dash for home:
He'd left without his socks.

Where have you been, Billy Boy?

Where have you been all the day, Billy Boy, Billy Boy?
Were you romping in the hay my Billy Boy?
I was out with Nancy Gray, sowing oats throughout the day.
And if kind Nancy tickles my fancy,
I'll be her charming Billy Boy.

And here's one for the smartest kid on the block...

Yellow Submarine

We all live in a yellow submarine.
It's highly claustrophobic,
And almost anaerobic.
But we don't care about fresh air,
As we're agoraphobic.